D1289883

100+ SOLOS
for
SAXOPHONE

Wise Publications
London/New York/Paris/Sydney

Exclusive Distributors:
Music Sales Limited
8/9 Frith Street,
London W1V 5TZ, England.

Music Sales Pty Limited
120 Rothschild Avenue,
Rosebery, NSW 2018,
Australia.

This book © Copyright 1992
by Wise Publications.
Order No.AM90025
ISBN 0-7119-3105-4

Cover design by Hutton Staniford.
Printed in the United Kingdom by
Caligraving Limited, Thetford, Norfolk.

Compiled by Peter Evans.
Music arranged by Steve Tayton.
Music processed by Upton & Skinner.

Instrument courtesy of Bill Lewington,
Shaftesbury Avenue, London WC2H 8NN.

Music Sales' complete catalogue lists
thousands of titles and is free from your
local music shop, or direct from
Music Sales Limited. Please send a
cheque/postal order for £1.50 for postage to:
Music Sales Limited, Newmarket Road,
Bury St. Edmunds, Suffolk IP33 3YB.

The Girl From Ipanema
(Garota De Ipanema)

Original Words by Vinicius De Moraes English Lyric by Norman Gimbel Music by Antonio Carlos Jobim

Perdido

Music by Juan Tizol Words by Harry Lenk and Ervin Drake

Wave

Words & Music by Antonio Carlos Jobim

Take The 'A' Train

Words & Music by Billy Strayhorn

5

One Note Samba
(Samba De Uma Nota So)

Original Words by N. Mendonca English Lyric by Jon Hendricks Music by Antonio Carlos Jobim

Slightly Out Of Tune
(Desafinado)

English Lyric by Jon Hendricks & Jessie Cavanaugh Music by Antonio Carlos Jobim

That Ole Devil Called Love

Words & Music by Doris Fisher & Allan Roberts

Take Five

By Paul Desmond

Solitude

Words by Eddie de Lange & Irving Mills Music by Duke Ellington

So Nice

Music & Original Lyrics by Marcos Valle & Paulo Sergio Valle English Lyrics by Norman Gimbel

I'm Beginning To See The Light

Words & Music by Harry James, Duke Ellington, Johnny Hodges & Don George

Medium bounce

Round Midnight

Words & Music by Cootie Williams & Thelonious Monk

Lullaby of Birdland

Music by George Shearing Words by George David Weiss

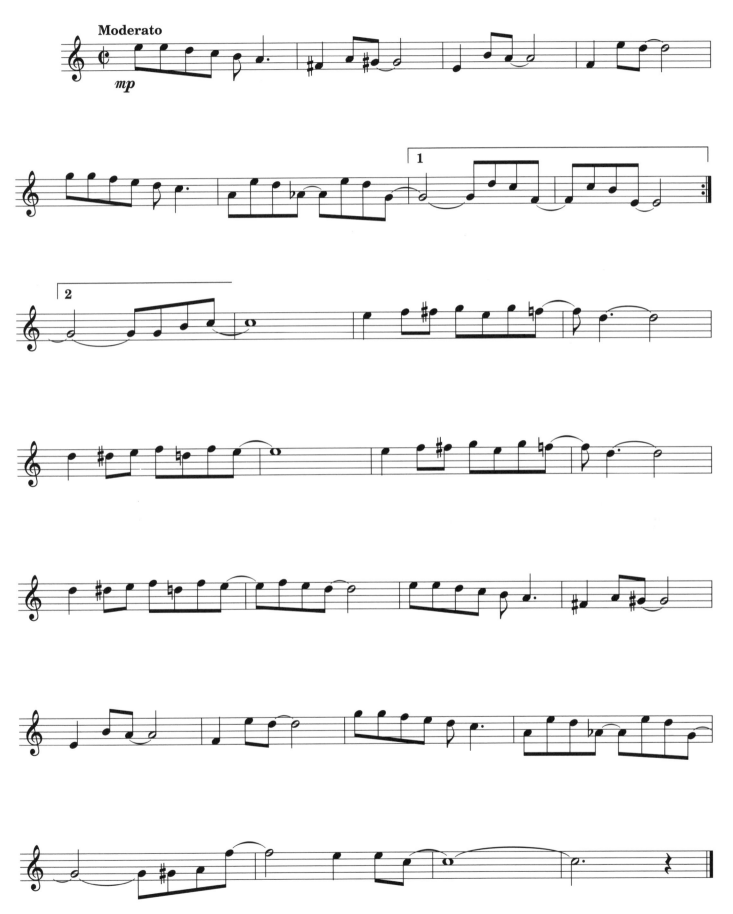

Satin Doll

Words by Johnny Mercer Music by Duke Ellington & Billy Strayhorn

All The Things You Are

Music by Jerome Kern Words by Oscar Hammerstein II

It Don't Mean A Thing
(If It Ain't Got That Swing)

Words by Irving Mills Music by Duke Ellington

Luck Be A Lady

Words & Music by Frank Loesser

I Believe In You

Words & Music by Frank Loesser

If My Friends Could See Me Now

Words by Dorothy Fields Music by Cy Coleman

Smoke Gets In Your Eyes

Music by Jerome Kern Words by Otto Harbach

Can't Help Lovin' Dat Man

Music by Jerome Kern Words by Oscar Hammerstein II

Woman

Words & Music by John Lennon

21

Standing On The Corner

Words & Music by Frank Loesser

I'll Never Fall In Love Again

Words by Hal David Music by Burt Bacharach

Ol' Man River

Music by Jerome Kern Words by Oscar Hammerstein II

I Know Him So Well

Words & Music by Benny Andersson, Tim Rice & Bjorn Ulvaeus

Till There Was You

Words & Music by Meredith Willson

I Dreamed A Dream
(From The Musical 'Les Misérables')

Music by Claude-Michel Schonberg Lyrics by Herbert Kretzmer Original Text by Alain Boublil & Jean-Marc Natel

Tonight

Music by Leonard Bernstein Lyrics by Stephen Sondheim

So Amazing

Words & Music by Luther Vandross

Repeat to fade

Seventy Six Trombones

Words & Music by Meredith Willson

Sit Down, You're Rocking The Boat

Words & Music by Frank Loesser

My Kind Of Girl

Words & Music by Leslie Bricusse

Send In The Clowns

Words & Music by Stephen Sondheim

I Don't Know How To Love Him

Music by Andrew Lloyd Webber Lyrics by Tim Rice

Nobody Does It Better

Words by Carole Bayer Sager Music by Marvin Hamlisch

Until It's Time For You To Go

Words & Music by Buffy Sainte-Marie

Don't Cry For Me Argentina

Music by Andrew Lloyd Webber Lyrics by Tim Rice

The First Time Ever I Saw Your Face

Words & Music by Ewan MacColl

O For The Wings Of A Dove

Composed by Felix Mendelssohn

Toreador's Song
(from 'Carmen')

Composed by Georges Bizet

La Donna È Mobile

Composed by Giuseppe Verdi

Fourth Movement Theme
('From The New World')

Composed by Antonin Dvořák

Land Of Hope & Glory
(Pomp & Circumstance March)

Composed by Sir Edward Elgar

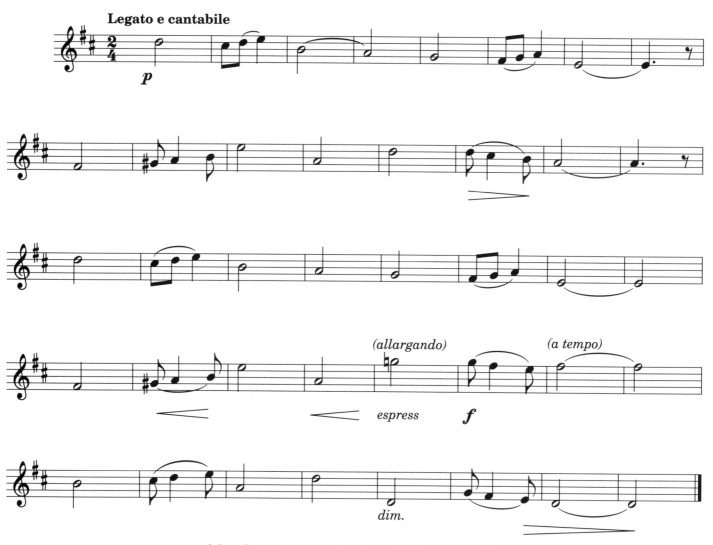

Jerusalem

Music by Hubert Parry Words by William Blake

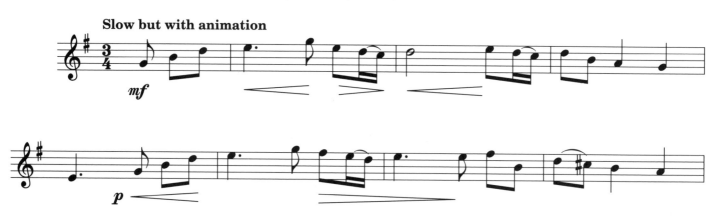

Theme From Swan Lake

Composed by Peter Ilyich Tchaikovsky

You've Got A Friend

Words & Music by Carole King

Your Song

Words & Music by Elton John and Bernie Taupin

Jupiter
(from 'The Planets Suite')

Composed by Gustav Holst

To All The Girls I've Loved Before

Words & Music by Hal David & Albert Hammond

This Guy's In Love With You

Words by Hal David Music by Burt Bacharach

Truly

Words & Music by Lionel Richie

When You're In Love With A Beautiful Woman

Words & Music by Even Stevens

Wonderful Tonight

Words & Music by Eric Clapton

Try A Little Tenderness

Words & Music by Harry Woods, Jimmy Campbell & Reg Connelly

The Wind Beneath My Wings

Words & Music by Jeff Silbar & Larry Henley

Unchained Melody

Music by Alex North Words by Hy Zaret

The Lady In Red

Words & Music by Chris De Burgh

On A Slow Boat To China

Words & Music by Frank Loesser

The Power Of Love

Words & Music by C.deRouge, G.Mende, J.Rush & S.Applegate

Caravan

By Duke Ellington, Irving Mills & Juan Tizol

A Night In Tunisia

Music by Frank Paparelli & John 'Dizzy' Gillespie Words by Raymond Leveen

Till Then

Words & Music by Guy Wood, Eddie Seller & Sol Marcus

Blue Rondo A La Turk

By Dave Brubeck

These Foolish Things

Words by Eric Maschwitz Music by Jack Strachey

The Very Thought Of You

Words & Music by Ray Noble

Strangers In The Night

Words by Charles Singleton & Eddie Snyder Music by Bert Kaempfert

There I've Said It Again

Words & Music by Redd Evans & Dave Mann

More Than I Can Say

Words & Music by Sonny Curtis & Jerry Allison

September Morn

Words & Music by Neil Diamond & Gilbert Becaud

The Mighty Quinn

Words & Music by Bob Dylan

66

Funny How Time Slips Away

Words & Music by Willie Nelson

It's Impossible
(Somos Novios)

Words by Sid Wayne Music by A. Manzanero

Somewhere

Music by Leonard Bernstein Lyrics by Stephen Sondheim

Love's Roundabout
(La Ronde De L'Amour)

French Words by Louis Ducreux English Words by Harold Purcell Music by Oscar Straus

If You Leave Me Now

Words & Music by Peter Cetera

An Old Fashioned Love Song

Words & Music by Paul Williams

Bye Bye Love

Words & Music by Felice & Boudleaux Bryant

Against All Odds
(Take A Look At Me Now)

Words & Music by Phil Collins

Just Like A Woman

Words & Music by Bob Dylan

I'll Be Your Baby Tonight

Words & Music by Bob Dylan

Something's Gotten Hold Of My Heart

Words & Music by Roger Cook & Roger Greenaway

It's Over

Words & Music by Roy Orbison & Bill Dees

How Deep Is Your Love

Words & Music by Barry Gibb, Robin Gibb & Maurice Gibb

We Don't Talk Anymore

Words & Music by Alan Tarney

As Time Goes By

Words & Music by Herman Hupfeld

I'm Stone In Love With You

Words & Music by T. Bell, L. Creed & A. Bell

If Not For You

Words & Music by Bob Dylan

(Moderately bright)

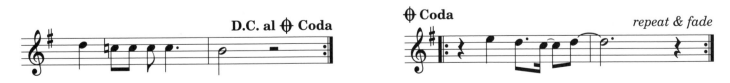

Moondance

Words & Music by Van Morrison

Missing You

Words & Music by Chris De Burgh

Let's Put It All Together

Words & Music by Hugo Peretti, Luigi Creatore, & George David Weiss

Crazy

Words & Music by Willie Nelson

Blowin' In The Wind

Words & Music by Bob Dylan

Love Is Blue
(L'Amour Est Bleu)

Music by André Popp Original Words by Pierre Cour English Lyric by Bryan Blackburn

Moderately slow

Softly Whispering I Love You

Words & Music by Roger Cook & Roger Greenaway

Lay, Lady, Lay

Words & Music by Bob Dylan

Feel Like Making Love

Words & Music by Eugene McDaniels

Memories Are Made Of This

Words & Music by Terry Gilkyson, Richard Dehr & Frank Miller

Forever Young

Words & Music by Bob Dylan

(Moderately slow, with a steady beat)

Right Here Waiting

Words & Music by Richard Marx

Endless Love

Words & Music by Lionel Richie

11/93 (16569)